PSYCHE & EROS

THE LADY AND THE MONSTER

**A
GREEK
MYTH**

GRAPHIC UNIVERSE™

STORY BY
MARIE CROALL

PENCILS AND INKS BY
RON RANDALL

EUROPE

ADRIATIC SEA

GREECE

▲ MOUNT OLYMPUS

AEGEAN SEA

MEDITERRANEAN SEA

PSYCHE & EROS

THE LADY AND THE MONSTER

BLACK SEA

A GREEK MYTH

ASIA MINOR

ORACLE AT DIDYMA

CYPRUS

LERNER BOOKS · LONDON · NEW YORK · MINNEAPOLIS

In Greek mythology, Mount Olympus is home to the most important gods and goddesses. These deities rule over nature and over all aspects of human life—such as love, marriage, death and the afterlife. The ancient Greek people honoured the gods and goddesses with prayer and gifts. In return, the deities interacted with human individuals, sometimes to the person's benefit and sometimes to his or her great misfortune.

Psyche is a mortal woman who gets drawn into the world of gods and goddesses. Her great beauty attracts both good and bad attention on Mount Olympus. She draws the jealous anger of Aphrodite, the goddess of love. At the same time, Psyche wins the love of Aphrodite's son, Eros, the god of passion. As many Greek myths do, Psyche's story weaves together human nature and divine power.

STORY BY MARIE CROALL

PENCILS AND INKS BY RON RANDALL

COLOURING BY HI-FI DESIGN

LETTERING BY MARSHALL DILLON AND TERRI DELGADO

CONSULTANT: THERESA KRIER, PH.D., MACALESTER COLLEGE

Graphic Universe™ is a trademark of Lerner Publishing Group, Inc.

First published in the United Kingdom in 2010 by Lerner Books, Dalton House, 60 Windsor Avenue, London SW19 2RR

Website address: www.lernerbooks.co.uk

This edition edited for UK publication in 2010.

British Library Cataloguing in Publication Data

Croall, Marie P.
Psyche & Eros : the lady and the monster.
1. Psyche (Greek deity)—Comic books, strips, etc.—Juvenile fiction. 2. Eros (Greek deity)—Comic books, strips, etc.--Juvenile fiction.
3. Children's stories—Comic books, strips, etc.
I. Title
741.5-dc22

ISBN-13: 978 0 7613 5394 2

Printed in China

TABLE OF CONTENTS

A BEAUTIFUL MAIDEN

THERE ONCE WAS A PROSPEROUS GREEK CITY.

THE CITY WAS RULED BY A WISE AND NOBLE MAN.

HE WAS A FAIR RULER. BUT MORE THAN HIS LAWS AND HIS CITY, HE WAS KNOWN FOR HIS DAUGHTERS.

THE ELDEST DAUGHTERS WERE PRETTY AND CHARMING.

BUT THE YOUNGEST, PSYCHE, WAS MORE BEAUTIFUL THAN ANY WOMAN WHO HAD EVER LIVED.

WORD OF PSYCHE'S GREAT BEAUTY SPREAD. CROWDS GATHERED TO CATCH A GLIMPSE OF HER.

YOU'D BETTER LEAVE, LITTLE SISTER.

FATHER'S TRYING TO TALK TO THE PEOPLE, BUT THE CROWD IS GROWING PUSHY.

ALL RIGHT. TELL FATHER I WENT TO THE TEMPLES.

PSYCHE'S SISTERS LOVED HER.

BUT SOMETIMES EVEN THEY GREW JEALOUS OF HER BEAUTY.

DID YOU SEE?

THAT'S HER!

WHEREVER PSYCHE WENT, PEOPLE STARED AND WHISPERED.

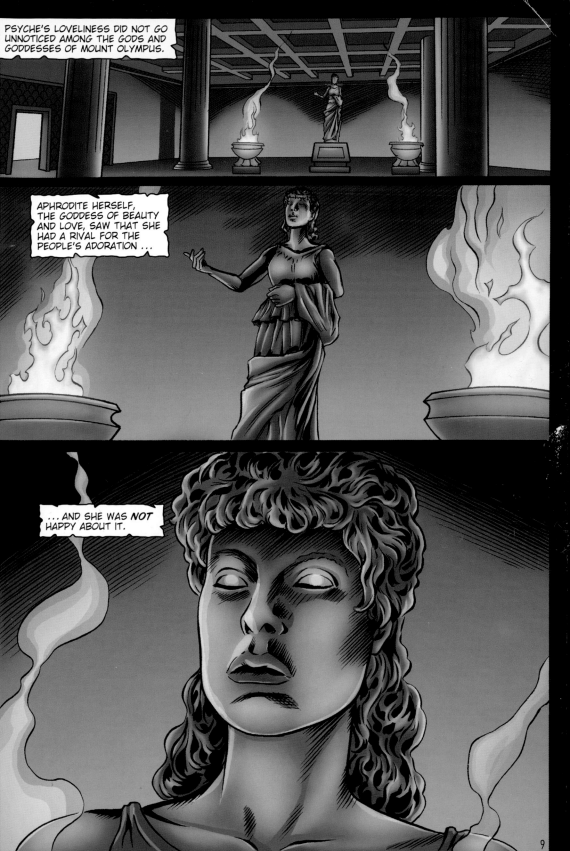

PSYCHE'S LOVELINESS DID NOT GO UNNOTICED AMONG THE GODS AND GODDESSES OF MOUNT OLYMPUS.

APHRODITE HERSELF, THE GODDESS OF BEAUTY AND LOVE, SAW THAT SHE HAD A RIVAL FOR THE PEOPLE'S ADORATION ...

... AND SHE WAS *NOT* HAPPY ABOUT IT.

ANXIOUS FOR AN ANSWER, THE KING JOURNEYED TO THE ORACLE.

HE HOPED THE PRIESTESS THERE WOULD BE ABLE TO TELL HIM IF THE PEOPLE'S ADORATION OF PSYCHE HAD OFFENDED THE GODS.

MANY PEOPLE CAME TO SEEK THE WISDOM OF THE ORACLE...

...AND THE KING PATIENTLY WAITED HIS TURN.

AT LAST, THE KING WAS BROUGHT BEFORE THE ORACLE'S PRIESTESS.

YOU HAVE COME BECAUSE OF YOUR DAUGHTER.

YES! WHAT IS HER FATE? WHAT HAVE THE GODS DECIDED FOR HER?

THE CREATURE PSYCHE WILL MARRY IS NOT HUMAN. HE IS A MONSTER WHOSE WHIMS CANNOT BE RESISTED.

A MONSTER? WHY!?

YOUR DAUGHTER MUST GO TO THE TOP OF THE MOUNTAIN OUTSIDE THE CITY. FROM THERE, SHE WILL BE TAKEN TO HER HUSBAND.

WITH A HEAVY HEART, THE KING BEGAN THE JOURNEY HOME...

...UNAWARE THAT HE WAS BEING WATCHED.

AT HOME, THE KING FOUND HIS WIFE AND DAUGHTER ANXIOUSLY AWAITING HIM.

WHAT IS IT, FATHER? WHAT DID YOU LEARN FROM THE ORACLE?

THE GODS HAVE A PLAN FOR YOU. IT IS THEIR WILL THAT YOU SHOULD MARRY A MONSTER.

A MONSTER?! OH, NO...

15

PSYCHE WAITED FOR A LONG TIME.

AND THEN...

...SOMEONE CAME FOR HER.

A MYSTERIOUS HUSBAND

BUT INSTEAD OF A HIDEOUS MONSTER...

...PSYCHE WAS GREETED BY ZEPHYRUS, GOD OF THE WEST WIND.

FORGIVE ME FOR KEEPING YOU WAITING.

SHALL I TAKE YOU TO YOUR HUSBAND NOW?

YES.

ZEPHYRUS EASILY LIFTED PSYCHE AND FLEW INTO THE TREACHEROUS CANYON.

AND BEFORE TOO LONG, THEY REACHED THEIR DESTINATION.

IT WAS THE MOST LAVISH PALACE PSYCHE HAD EVER SEEN.

PSYCHE WAS COMFORTED BY HIS WORDS BUT STILL WORRIED. WHO WAS HER MYSTERIOUS HUSBAND?

YOUR HUSBAND WILL COME TO SEE YOU TONIGHT.

HAVE NO FEAR. ALL WILL BE WELL.

PSYCHE WANDERED THOUGH THE PALACE... ...AWED BY ITS BEAUTY AND SPLENDOUR.

SHE FOUND THE LARGEST BEDROOM.

EXHAUSTED FROM THE DAY'S EVENTS, SHE FELL ASLEEP.

A PARADISE LOST

PSYCHE WAITED IN VAIN FOR HER HUSBAND TO RETURN.

SHE STOPPED SLEEPING AND EATING.

ALL SHE THOUGHT OF WAS HER BELOVED EROS.

AT LAST, PSYCHE DECIDED THAT IF SHE WANTED HER HUSBAND BACK, SHE WOULD HAVE TO FIND HIM.

SHE SET OFF IN SEARCH OF HIM.

SHE SEARCHED IN TEMPLES IN THE CITIES.

SHE SEARCHED IN TEMPLES BY THE OCEANS.

BUT SHE FOUND NOTHING.

FINALLY, PSYCHE WENT TO THE FOOT OF MOUNT OLYMPUS, THE HOME OF THE GODS. SHE WOULD SEEK HELP FROM THE OLYMPIAN GODDESSES.

FIRST, PSYCHE TURNED TO DEMETER, THE GODDESS OF GRAIN AND OF THE HARVEST.

GODDESS DEMETER, YOUR OWN DAUGHTER, PERSEPHONE, IS REUNITED WITH HER HUSBAND, HADES, EVERY WINTER.

PLEASE REUNITE ME WITH MY BELOVED EROS.

I CAN HEAR YOU, CHILD, AND I WOULD HELP YOU IF I COULD.

BUT APHRODITE'S WRATH IS NOT SOMETHING I CAN WITHSTAND.

I CAN DO NOTHING FOR YOU.

PSYCHE TURNED NEXT TO HERA, THE GODDESS OF MARRIAGE.

HERA, YOU ARE THE PROTECTOR OF ALL MARRIED WOMEN.

PLEASE HELP ME FIND MY HUSBAND.

CHILD, THIS IS NOTHING I CAN HELP YOU WITH.

I HAVE NO TIME FOR APHRODITE'S JEALOUSY.

THERE'S NO AID FOR ME HERE.

I KNOW WHAT I MUST DO NOW.

PLEASE, GODDESS, I NEVER MEANT TO OFFEND YOU.

I LOVE HIM...

PLEASE.

APHRODITE DECIDED NOT TO SEND THE GIRL AWAY. SHE THOUGHT OF SOMETHING WORSE INSTEAD.

AFTER YOU WORK FOR ME...

AS MY SERVANT.

I WILL HELP YOU.

I'LL DO ANYTHING TO FIND EROS.

IMPOSSIBLE TASKS

PSYCHE GREW WORRIED ABOUT WHAT APHRODITE HAD IN STORE FOR HER.

FOLLOW ME.

APHRODITE PUT PSYCHE TO WORK RIGHT AWAY.

THE GODDESS TOOK THE GIRL TO A ROOM DEEP IN THE TEMPLE.

THE ENORMOUS ROOM WAS FILLED WITH SEEDS.

ALL THESE DIFFERENT KINDS OF SEEDS MUST BE SORTED INTO SEPARATE PILES.

I WILL RETURN IN A DAY.

SEE THAT YOUR TASK IS FINISHED BY THEN.

THIS IS IMPOSSIBLE. I CAN'T DO THIS ALONE IN A DAY!

YET I HAVE NO CHOICE BUT TO TRY.

HOURS PASSED, AND PSYCHE MADE LITTLE PROGRESS.

PSYCHE BEGAN TO DREAD APHRODITE'S RETURN.

WHAT WOULD THE ANGRY GODDESS DO WHEN SHE SAW THAT PSYCHE HAD FAILED?

BUT THEN...

MAY WE BE OF ASSISTANCE?

ASSISTANCE? YOU?

YES, WE CAN HELP YOU.

A GOOD FRIEND ASKED US TO.

A FRIEND...

THE ANTS HEADED STRAIGHT TO THE PILES.

THEY WORKED QUICKLY, SORTING EACH PILE OF SEED.

SOON THE ANTS HAD FINISHED APHRODITE'S TASK.

I AM SO GRATEFUL TO YOU.

HOW CAN I REPAY YOU?

DO NOT WORRY. WE WERE HAPPY TO HELP.

SHE IS COMING.

PSYCHE SAFELY GATHERED THE FLEECE.

SHE RETURNED TO APHRODITE...

...WHO WAS LESS THAN HAPPY TO SEE THE IMPOSSIBLE TASK COMPLETED.

BEFORE SHE KNEW IT, PSYCHE FOUND HERSELF STANDING BEFORE HADES AND HIS QUEEN, PERSEPHONE.

PSYCHE TOLD THEM WHY SHE HAD COME TO THE UNDERWORLD. BUT HADES WAS UNMOVED BY HER PLEA.

YOU HAVE GIVEN ME NO REASON TO AID YOU, MORTAL.

HUSBAND!

CAN YOU NOT SEE THAT SHE IS IN LOVE?

SHE WANTS ONLY TO FIND HER HUSBAND.

HADES, THIS MORTAL IS WORTHY OF OUR AID.

WELL, I SUPPOSE...

HERE IS THE BEAUTY YOU SEEK.

DOWN HERE, WE DO NOT FEAR APHRODITE'S WRATH.

I AM SO GRATEFUL. I CANNOT TELL YOU HOW MUCH...

YOU ARE MOST WELCOME. FIND CHARON AGAIN, AND HE WILL FERRY YOU BACK TO EARTH.

GLOSSARY

APHRODITE: the Greek goddess of love

CERBERUS: a fierce, three-headed dog that guards the entrance to the underworld

CHARON: the boatman who guides souls across the river Styx into the underworld

CYPRUS: an island in the Mediterranean Sea near Turkey. Cyprus was traditionally thought to be the home of Aphrodite.

DEMETER: the Greek goddess of the harvest and of agriculture

EROS: Aphrodite's son and the Greek god of passion

HADES: the Greek god of the underworld

HERA: the Greek goddess of marriage and childbirth, married to Zeus

MOUNT OLYMPUS: a mountain in north eastern Greece. The ancient Greeks believed the mountain was home to the gods and goddesses, who each had a palace there.

NAIAD: in Greek myth, a type of female spirit who lives in rivers, streams, springs and other bodies of fresh running water

ORACLE: speech in which a god reveals a hidden truth or foretells a future event, or the place where that happens. The ancient Greeks believed that the gods spoke through special priestesses who lived in temples or in isolated places, such as caves.

PERSEPHONE: Demeter's daughter and Hades's wife

PSYCHE: a beautiful princess who falls in love with Eros

STYX: the river that encircles the underworld. Once the souls of the dead were ferried across the Styx by Charon, they could not return to the world above.

UNDERWORLD: the kingdom of the dead, ruled over by Hades. In Greek mythology, the souls of the dead travelled to the underworld, where Hades decided their eternal fate. Living mortals were not allowed in the underworld.

ZEPHYRUS: the Greek god of the west wind

ZEUS: the main Greek god, the ruler of Mount Olympus

FURTHER READING

Bolton, Lesley. *The Everything Classical Mythology Book: Greek and Roman Gods, Goddesses, Heroes, and Monsters from Ares to Zeus.* Avon, MA: Adams Media Corporation, 2010. This who's who guide introduces young readers to Greek and Roman mythology.

Claybourne, Anna and Rodney Matthews. *Greek Myths and Legends.* London: Usborne Publishing Ltd, 2007. This is a new edition of this detailed introduction to the most famous gods and goddesses in Greek mythology and their exploits. Fully illustrated throughout, this title helps the reader understand the stories of the Greek gods and the way in which they were worshipped. A full index and Who's Who section at the back of this book make it a must for those studying mythology or researching for a project.

Evans, Cheryl and Anne Millard. *The Usborne Illustrated Guide to Myths and Legends.* London: Usborne Publishing Ltd, 1985. Identifies the gods, goddesses, heroes and monsters of Greek mythology, recounts the most famous stories and briefly describes Greek history and culture.

Hamilton, Edith. *Mythology.* Boston: Little, Brown & Co., 1942. Hamilton's classic book focuses on the stories of Greek gods and heroes, but it also covers Roman and Norse myths.

Limke, Jeff and Tim Seeley. *Jason: Quest for the Golden Fleece.* London: Lerner Books, 2008. The story of how Jason returns to claim his birthright and the challenges he faces.

Phillip, Neil. *Mythology.* London: Dorris Kindersley Publishing, 2005. This volume uses dozens of colourful pictures and photographs to explore myths from around the world.

CREATING *PSYCHE & EROS*

In retelling Psyche's tale, Marie Croall drew upon classical and modern sources including *The Story of Eros and Psyche* by Apuleius, translated by Edward Carpenter. Artist Ron Randall used books on ancient Greek history, clothing, and architecture and photographs of Greek art to shape the story's visual details. And consultant Theresa Krier provided expert guidance on historical details, textual accuracy, and classical pronunciation.

original pencil sketch from page 6

INDEX

ABOUT THE AUTHOR AND THE ARTIST

MARIE P. CROALL lives in Cary, North Carolina, with her husband and four cats. She has written for Marvel, DC Comics, Moonstone Books, Devil's Due, and Harris Comics. Her other Graphic Myths and Legends work includes *Ali Baba: Fooling the Forty Thieves*, *Marwe: Into the Land of the Dead*, and *Sinbad: Sailing into Peril*. She has also completed a self-published graphic novel and a short film. She has spent much of her life reading fables and legends and enjoys discovering new things about different cultures.

RON RANDALL has drawn comics for every major comic publisher in the United States, including Marvel, DC, Image, and Dark Horse. His Graphic Myths and Legends work includes *Thor & Loki: In the Land of Giants*, *Amaterasu: Return of the Sun*, *Beowulf: Monster Slayer*, and *Tristan & Isolde: The Warrior and the Princess*. He has also worked on superhero comics such as *Justice League* and *Spiderman*; science fiction titles such as *Star Wars* and *Star Trek*; fantasy adventure titles such as *DragonLance* and *Warlord*; suspense and horror titles including *Swamp Thing*, *Predator*, and *Venom*; and his own creation, *Trekker*. He lives in Portland, Oregon.

First published in the United States of America in 2009